...I HAVE TO DO THE UNTHINKABLE.
HE'S GONNA SHOOT THE KID!
TAKE THE GUN OFF THE BOY OR WE WILL DROP YOU!
BANG
BANG
POLICE
BANG
BANG
BANG
BANG
BULLETS AREN'T GOING TO KILL A DEMON...

IT'S STILL BEHIND US!

TURN INTO THE PARK!

I CAN'T TURN INTO THE PARK! THERE ARE GIANT CONCRETE BOLLARDS STOPPING--

TURN!

JOHN! YOU FUCKER!

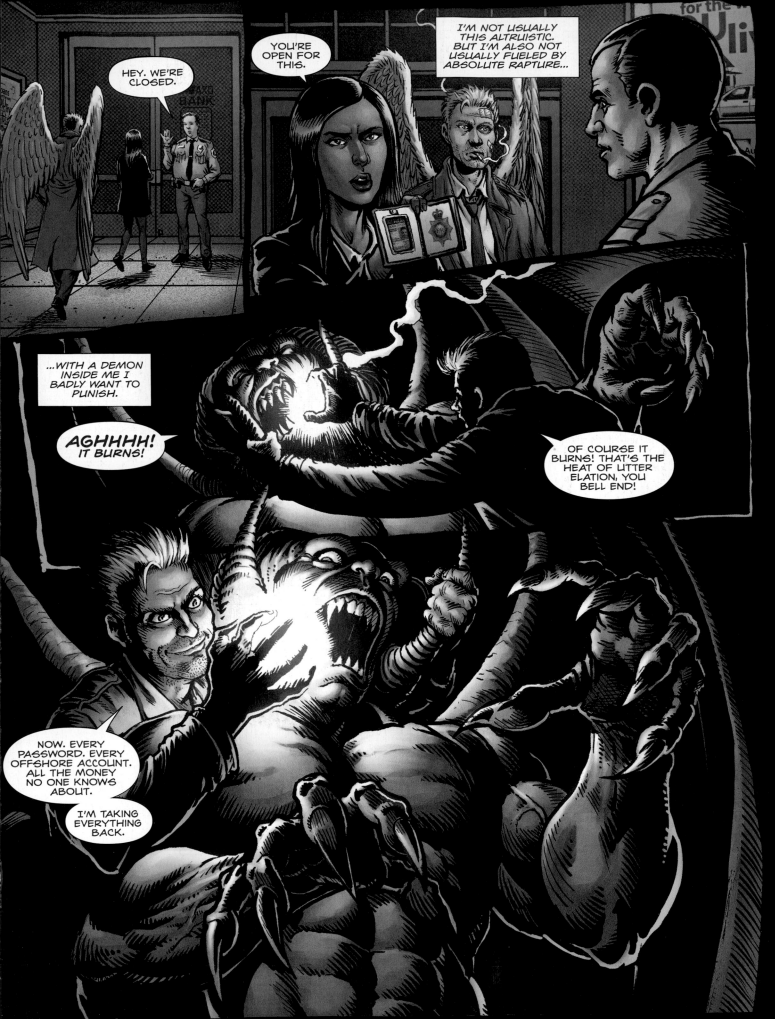

HELLBLAZER
RISE and FALL

UNUSED COVER SKETCH
FOR ISSUE #3

ORIGINAL PITCH SKETCH

DC

BLACK
LABEL

UNUSED COVER FOR ISSUE #1

ART BY

DARICK ROBERTSON